The Soil Neighborhood

By

Dan Yunk
&
Steve Swaffar

"Kailey, it's time to come in, take a bath, and get ready for bed," Grandma said.

"Grandma, I like coming to stay with you, but I don't like to take baths!"

3

4

"I sure wish there wasn't any dirt because I wouldn't have to take baths anymore!" Kailey explained.

"Oh gosh, Kailey, dirt is really important to humans and especially our farmer friends in their production of wheat, corn and soybeans. That's why they take such good care of the land."

"Let me tell you a little story while you take your bath about why dirt, or let's call it soil, is so important."

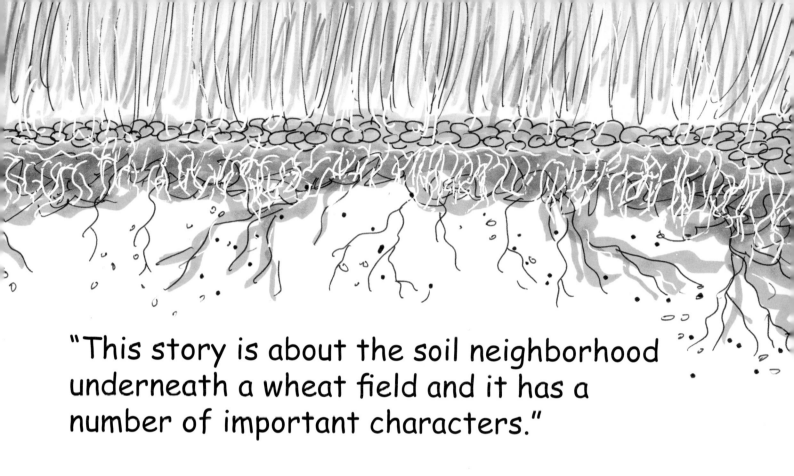

"This story is about the soil neighborhood underneath a wheat field and it has a number of important characters."

Clay and his friends Rocky and Sandy live in the soil neighborhood below the surface of the earth.

There are lots of families in the neighborhood who work together to make the soil a good place to live and grow.

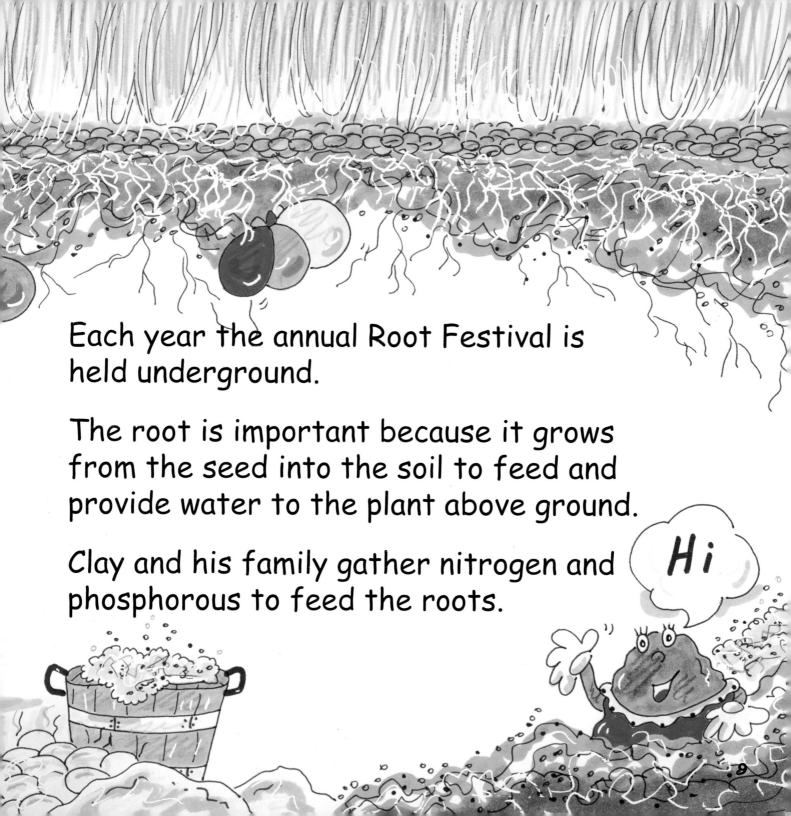

Each year the annual Root Festival is held underground.

The root is important because it grows from the seed into the soil to feed and provide water to the plant above ground.

Clay and his family gather nitrogen and phosphorous to feed the roots.

Hi

Phosphorous and nitrogen provide energy and food to the plant and help it mature and grow.

Rocky and his family provide other minerals like potassium, iron, and zinc that the plant needs.

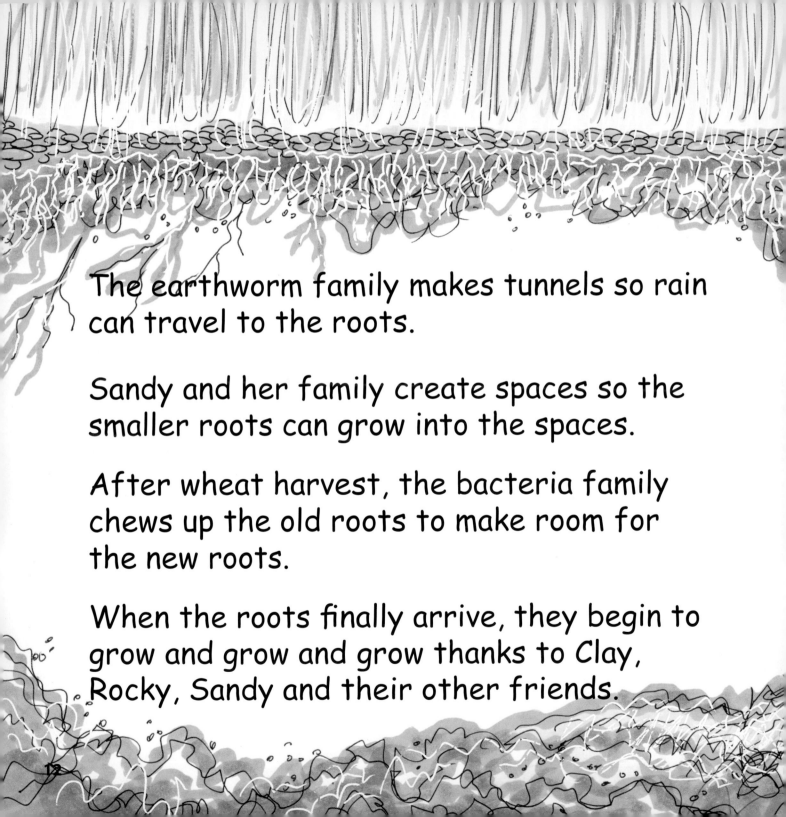

The earthworm family makes tunnels so rain can travel to the roots.

Sandy and her family create spaces so the smaller roots can grow into the spaces.

After wheat harvest, the bacteria family chews up the old roots to make room for the new roots.

When the roots finally arrive, they begin to grow and grow and grow thanks to Clay, Rocky, Sandy and their other friends.

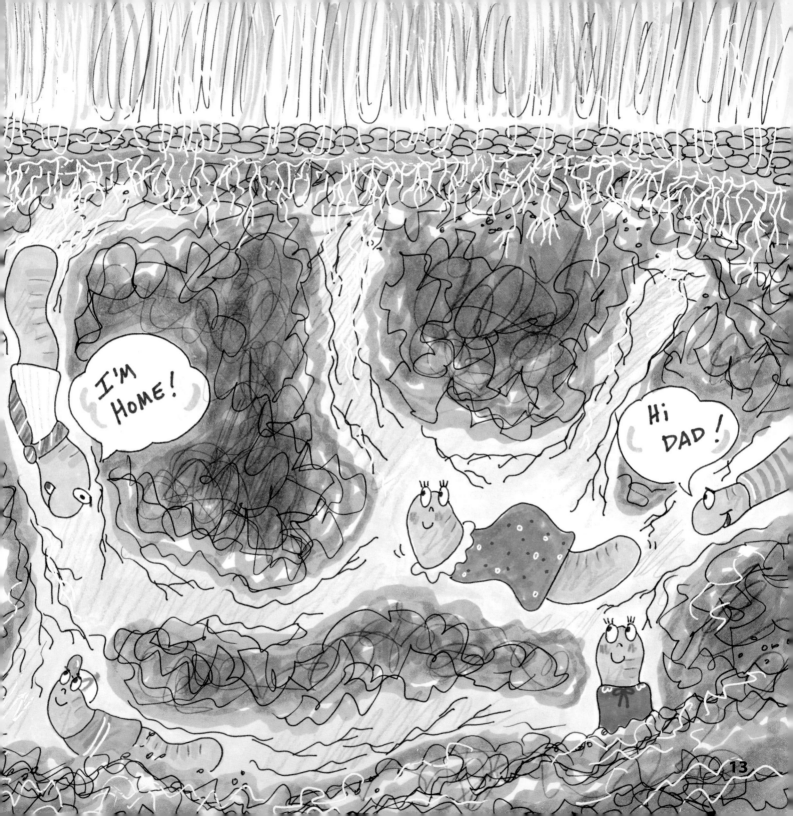

14

Once, the hard work of all these underground families is complete, farmers will harvest the crops and will provide us things we use everyday: food, clothing, crayons and even soap for your bath, Kailey.

"Wow, Grandma! I see now why soil is so important to us."

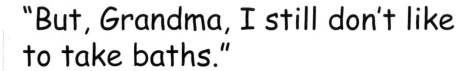

"But, Grandma, I still don't like to take baths."

"Kailey, just like you appreciate soil now after learning more about it, I bet you'll learn to enjoy a nice, warm bath as you get older."

"OK, Grandma. I bet you're right but actually I can wait awhile for that to happen."